# The Family Pack of Questionnaires and Scales

A Cox and A Bentovim

Department of Health

# The Family Pack of Questionnaires and Scales

## A Cox and A Bentovim

London
The Stationery Office

## Social Care Group

The Social Care Group is one of the four business groups in the Department of Health. It is jointly headed by the Chief Social Services Inspector and the Head of Social Care Policy. It supports Ministers in promoting high quality, cost effective services through

- national policies

- support to external social care agencies

- inspection

The Social Services Inspectorate is a part of the Social Care Group. It is headed by the Chief Social Services Inspector who is the principal professional advisor to Ministers on social services and related matters.

ISBN 011 322426 5

Published by The Stationery Office Ltd

Applications for reproduction should be made in writing to:
The Copyright Unit
Her Majesty's Stationery Office
St Clements House
2–16 Colegate
Norwich NR3 1BQ

Printed in the United Kingdom for The Stationery Office

# Contents

# Assessing the Needs of Children and Families: Using Questionnaires and Scales

## 1    Introduction

This pack, which accompanies the Framework for the Assessment of Children in Need and their Families (2000), sets out how a number of questionnaires and scales can be used by social work and other social services staff when assessing children and their families. The materials were piloted in a number of child care situations within five social service departments and modified to suit children and families and the requirements of staff working in this setting. The instruments can assist staff preparing reports for the Court, by providing a clear evidence base for the judgements and recommendations made regarding a child, and inform the child care plan.

## 2    Summary of Questionnaires and Scales

The following eight questionnaires and scales are included in the pack:

2.1    **The Strengths and Difficulties Questionnaires** (Goodman, 1997; Goodman *et al*, 1998). These scales are a modification of the very widely used instruments to screen for emotional and behavioural problems in children and adolescents – the Rutter A + B scales for parents and teachers. Although similar to Rutter's, the Strengths and Difficulties Questionnaire's wording was re-framed to focus on a child's emotional and behavioural strengths as well as difficulties. The actual questionnaire incorporates five scales: pro-social, hyperactivity, emotional problems, conduct (behavioural) problems, and peer problems. In the pack, there are versions of the scale to be completed by adult caregivers, or teachers for children from age 3 to 16, and young people between the ages of 11–16. These questionnaires have been used with disabled children and their teachers and carers. They are available in 40 languages on the following website: *http://chp.iop.kcl.ac.uk/sdq/b3.html*

2.2    **The Parenting Daily Hassles Scale** (Crnic and Greenberg, 1990; Crnic and Booth, 1991). This scale aims to assess the frequency and intensity/impact of 20 potential parenting 'daily' hassles experienced by adults caring for children. It has been used in a wide variety of research studies concerned with children and families – particularly families with young children. It has been found that parents (or caregivers) generally like filling it out, because it touches on many aspects of being a parent that are important to them.

2.3    **Home Conditions Scale** (The Family Cleanliness Scale. Davie et al, 1984) addresses various aspects of the home environment (for example, smell, state of surfaces in house, floors). The total score has been found to correlate highly with indices of the development of children.

2.4 **Adult Wellbeing Scale** (Irritability, Depression, Anxiety – IDA Scale. Snaith *et al*, 1978). This scale looks at how an adult is feeling in terms of depression, anxiety and irritability. The questions are framed in a 'personal' fashion (i.e. I feel..., My appetite is...). The scale allows the adult to respond from four possible answers.

2.5 **The Adolescent Wellbeing Scale** (Self-rating Scale for Depression in Young People. Birleson, 1980). It was originally validated for children aged between 7–16. It involves 18 questions each relating to different aspects of a child or adolescent's life, and how they feel about these. As a result of the pilot the wording of some questions was altered in order to be more appropriate to adolescents. Although children as young as seven and eight have used it, older children's thoughts and beliefs about themselves are more stable. The scale is intended to enable practitioners to gain more insight and understanding into how an adolescent feels about their life.

2.6 **The Recent Life Events Questionnaire** This scale was taken from Brugha *et al* (1985), with nine additional items added. It focuses on recent life events (ie. those occurring in the last 12 months) but could be used over a longer time-scale. It is intended to assist in the compilation of a social history. Respondents are asked to identify which of the events still affects them. It is intended that use of the scale will:

- result in a fuller picture of a family's history and contribute to greater contextual understanding of the family's current situation;

- help practitioners explore how particular recent life events have affected the carer and the family;

- in some situations, identify life events which family members have not reported earlier.

2.7 **The Family Activity Scale** (Derived from The Child-Centredness Scale. Smith, 1985). These scales give practitioners an opportunity to explore with carers the environment provided for their children, through joint activities and support for independent activities. This includes information about the cultural and ideological environment in which children live, as well as how their carers respond to their children's actions (for example, concerning play and independence). They aim to be independent of socio-economic resources. There are two separate scales; one for children aged 2–6, and one for children aged 7–12.

2.8 **The Alcohol Scale** This scale was developed by Piccinelli et al (1997). Alcohol abuse is estimated to be present in about 6% of primary carers, ranking it third in frequency behind major depression and generalised anxiety. Higher rates are found in certain localities, and particularly amongst those parents known to social services departments. Drinking alcohol affects different individuals in different ways. For example, some people may be relatively unaffected by the same amount of alcohol that incapacitates others. The primary concern therefore is not the amount of alcohol consumed, but how it impacts on the individual and, more particularly, on their role as a parent. This questionnaire has been found to be effective in detecting individuals with alcohol disorders and those with hazardous drinking habits.

## 3    Principles underpinning the use of the questionnaires and scales

3.1    **Clarity of Purpose.** Clarity about aims is fundamental to all assessment. In practice these can be broad ranging or more focused, depending on timing and context, but in general there will be an intention to gather a range of relevant information in a manner that promotes, or sustains, a working relationship with the children and families being assessed: in most circumstances information is of limited use if collaboration has broken down.

3.2    **Assessment is not a static process.** The process of assessment should be therapeutic. An assessment has many purposes. It should inform future work, and evaluate the progress of interventions. The way in which the assessment is carried out is also important. It should enable those involved to gain fresh perspectives on their family situation, which are in themselves therapeutic.

3.3    **Partnership is informed by professional judgement.** It follows that, although partnership is a fundamental principle, this does not mean that every detail of information gained, or in particular the practitioners judgement about that information, is shared immediately and in full with those being assessed. Sustaining partnership and positive therapeutic impact are overriding principles.

3.4    **Assessment does not take place in a vacuum.** Assessments benefit from multiple sources of information, and multiple methods. Any one source used alone is likely to give either a limited or unbalanced view. This applies to all the main approaches: interviewing, observation, and the use of standardised tests and questionnaires. Limitations should be recognised. Contrasting data from different methods and/ or sources is vital to develop a deeper and more balanced understanding of the situation.

## 4    Background

4.1    Many practitioners will be unfamiliar with the use of instruments in day-to-day practice. They are often thought to be limited, judgmental, and superficial. However these are dangers with all assessment approaches. The vital issue is **how and when** an approach is used.

4.2    Standardised Questionnaires and Scales must be distinguished from Standardised and Semi-structured interviews. Questionnaires are (usually) brief, use set questions, and are frequently designed to be completed by a respondent – a person who is being assessed or contributing to the assessment, but is not themselves the professional with responsibility for pulling together the whole picture.

4.3    The respondent does not have to interact directly with the assessor while they are completing the questionnaire and can, therefore, concentrate on **voicing their needs** and concerns unimpeded. Indeed, there is evidence that responses to questionnaires can be more frank than in an interview.

4.4    Although most questionnaires have been designed to be completed by respondents, they can be used in other ways, for example as **mental check-lists** for the assessor, either with regard to what they observe or what they take up with the respondent. They can be administered verbally, or provide prompts that are the basis for further discussion.

4.5    In whatever ways they have been used or presented in day-to-day practice, question-naires should always prompt discussion between worker and respondent. To pick up the questionnaire and leave, or ask the questions and just note the answers is not appropriate, although as a questionnaire is administered verbally it may be best to keep fuller discussions to the end.

4.6    Many questionnaires have been designed to screen for particular problems or needs. They have been standardised so that a score above a particular cut-off indicates the strong probability of a significant problem of the type for which the questionnaire is screening. This can be a useful guideline, but it must be remembered that scores above or below a particular cut-off do not guarantee the presence or absence of a significant problem in the individual case. Further discussion can help to clarify whether respondents are over-or-under-representing their needs. Furthermore, there may be highly significant needs picked up by individual questions, even when the overall score is well below the cut-off.

4.7    Questionnaires can not only be used in different ways, they can be used with different respondents, for example, foster or birth parents, residential or nursery workers, children or young people and in different contexts.

## 5    Testing the use of the questionnaires and scales in practice

5.1    The questionnaires and scales in this pack have been piloted by staff in a variety of settings – metropolitan, urban and rural – with adult carers of children and young people, and with some children and young people themselves. The children involved were children in need (section 17 of the Children Act, 1989): they included children who were living with their families and children who were accommodated including those who were experiencing respite care. Some of these children were being assessed as part of s47 enquiries and the names of some other children were on a child protection register. The children's needs were varied; physical, cognitive, education and behavioural. Most children had behavioural needs alone or in combination with other needs.

5.2    During piloting practitioners took time to get acclimatised to the use of the question-naires, and indeed how to use them most effectively, but increasingly found them easy to administer and of immediate benefit. For example, they revealed needs of which staff were unaware, or modified their views of needs with which they were already familiar. Often there was increased understanding of the nature and extent of the problems facing family members. One of the instruments, the Recent Life Events Questionnaire, raised new issues on three quarters of the occasions it was used: for several other questionnaires it was more than half the times they were given.

5.3    The questionnaire proved helpful both for initial and core assessments and for reviewing progress. The context of some instruments provided a valuable focus for work with the families.

5.4    In many cases use of the questionnaires and scales helped consolidate the relationship between the staff member and family. Children and parents reported that they liked filling in the questionnaires and scales.

# 6    The use of the Questionnaires and Scales in practice

**When should I use a questionnaire/scale?**

6.1    Practitioners have to decide when and why they are going to use a particular questionnaire or scale. Piloting suggested they can be of use in almost any context, even those where the practitioner considers they already have a good grasp of the family's needs. However, questions were raised about their appropriateness in several particular circumstances.

6.2    For example, sometimes it felt inappropriate to use questionnaires where the problems potentially tapped by the instruments were not at all evident, but it is in **these** circumstances that they may be of particular value in providing a way to bring out what the respondent has thought irrelevant or been reluctant to divulge.

Where certain problems are not evident, those that **are** can be acknowledged and summarised. The questionnaire can then be introduced as a way of speedily checking out another area before discussing it in more detail if appropriate.

6.3    On occasions, it was also considered insensitive to present a questionnaire when needs in a particular area were **very** evident. In practice it often offered a way to obtain a fuller understanding or established a baseline for measuring improvement.

One approach is to summarise what the practitioner and respondent already share and explain that the questionnaire may do just that, acknowledge the extent of current understanding, or help to mark the present situation so that progress can be readily established.

6.4    Emergencies and crises were considered to be occasions when respondents would not have enough time and mental space to address a form. However, even when there is a crisis there are times when professionals are consulting with each other and carers or children are waiting. Appropriately presented a questionnaire can help carers or children feel that they are still active partners, and that the professionals are still listening.

**What about when working with disabled children?**

6.5    Staff working with disabled children, including those with learning disabilities, had reservations about giving carers forms concerned with children's behaviour or family activities. This was because they felt the carers would feel judged adversely for not providing an adequate range of activities for their child, or blamed for the child's behaviour. This reticence demonstrates that it is vital that the instruments are presented as ways to understand families' concerns or difficulties, not to judge them. Behavioural problems are particularly prevalent amongst disabled children, and it is especially hard to organise a full range of family activities with such children. If these facts are acknowledged to the carers, and it is explained that the questionnaire is a basis for discussion of how matters may be improved, for example how other activities might be arranged with Social Services support, then the instruments can be useful.

**How do I introduce the questionnaires to families?**

6.6    Whenever a questionnaire is introduced, it is not just a matter of considering its appropriateness, but explaining its purpose and potential relevance. The respondent should also be able to comprehend where it fits into the assessment as a whole and how it may be able to extend understanding of the current family situation.

**What other purposes can I use a questionnaire for?**

6.7 Certain questionnaires may be useful as mental checklists, either for observation or structuring discussion with the respondent. For example, this applies to the Home Conditions Scale and Alcohol Use Questionnaire. Social services staff should assess the family's physical environment. The Home Conditions Scale is a list of items that can be used in isolation from, for example, an evaluation of the quality of the parent-child relationship. However, it provides a guideline as research has found the total score to be strongly correlated with child cognitive development. In addition, the individual items can point to specific targets to work on if there is a concern that the lack of cleanliness is a danger to the child. Establishing whether the family can work to achieve these targets is another way that this and some of the other scales can be used.

6.8 In summary, a questionnaire can be introduced as a way of understanding the families' or individual members' needs or to acknowledge the extent of current shared knowledge of the family's predicament. With some it may be relevant to indicate, at the outset, that the questionnaire may provide suggestions for the support the family requires, or aspects that the carer and social worker can work on together.

## 7 Using information gathered to inform work with the family

7.1 Unless the questionnaire has been used simply as a mental checklist, it should be discussed with the respondent. Discussion should cover their overall thoughts and feelings about completing it, and individual items which raise possible issues or indicate improvements.

In piloting several practitioners mentioned the value of the questionnaire in making progress.

7.2 Discussion is probably best at the completion of the questionnaire, whether administered verbally or filled in by the respondent, but there will be times when it is important to pick up individual items during completion if they are of very immediate significance. For example, some carers were unhappy about the question on self-harm in the Adult Wellbeing scale. Their concerns need to be understood. If such a question is disturbing it could well mean that the respondent worries that they will be thought inadequate as a parent, or that they have indeed had thoughts of injuring themselves.

7.3 Thus practitioners should be prepared to take up issues that arise, whether indicators of needs or progress. In piloting some workers commented that observing the respondent and the way they completed the questionnaire was also valuable. It is important to remain alert while the instrument is being filled out.

7.4 When respondents are unsure of the meaning of individual items it is better to find out what they think it means before attempting to clarify, but the practitioner must be prepared to explain if necessary. In doing so, it is worth remembering that mutual understanding between family member and worker is more important than whether a form is correctly filled in.

7.5    If there has not been an opportunity to do so, the practitioner should remember to explain how using the instrument fits into broader assessment work, whenever appropriate.

7.6    Piloting suggests that it is often useful and good for the worker-family member relationship, if they score the questionnaire together, but acknowledgement of the needs expressed is the priority for further work.

7.7    Sometimes it may be appropriate to emphasis the questionnaire's screening status, and that definite conclusions should not be reached on the basis of one form. However, it is important to keep the door open to the possibility of significant needs, even if the information derived from the questionnaire does not appear to fit with other knowledge about the family.

       Where needs are mutually accepted by social worker and respondent, it will not be necessary to reassure the family member.

7.8    There will be times when issues raised require the practitioner to consult with others, for example if the respondent expresses thought of self-harm, or the child has marked emotional and behavioural problems that might merit referral to another agency. As in other circumstances this will require discussion.

7.9    The questionnaire should not be administered to the same individual, or about the same individual too frequently. Responses may become less valid, or respondents irritated. At least a 3 month gap is recommended.

## 8    The Family Assessment Pack of Questionnaires and Scales

8.1    Each questionnaire and scale is set out in the following pages, with accompanying guidance on its use. Where appropriate, the scoring system is included separately.

8.2    The questionnaires and scales have been included in the pack also in a form for ease of photocopying. They are intended to be photocopied back-to-back and folded for use with children and families.

# Strengths and Difficulties

## QUESTIONNAIRES

# **Strengths and Difficulties**
## QUESTIONNAIRE

## TO BE COMPLETED BY A MAIN CARER OF A CHILD AGED BETWEEN 3 AND 4

For each item, please mark the box for Not True, Somewhat True or Certainly True. It would help us if you answered all items as best you can even if you are not absolutely certain, or the items seem daft! Please give your answers on the basis of the child's behaviour over the last six months.

Child's Name _____   Male/Female   Date of Birth _____

| | Not True | Somewhat True | Certainly True |
|---|---|---|---|
| Considerate of other people's feelings | ☐ | ☐ | ☐ |
| Restless, overactive, cannot stay still for long | ☐ | ☐ | ☐ |
| Often complains of headaches, stomach-aches or sickness | ☐ | ☐ | ☐ |
| Shares readily with other children (treats, toys, pencils etc.) | ☐ | ☐ | ☐ |
| Often has temper tantrums or hot tempers | ☐ | ☐ | ☐ |
| Rather solitary, tends to play alone | ☐ | ☐ | ☐ |
| Generally obedient, usually does what adults request | ☐ | ☐ | ☐ |
| Many worries, often seems worried | ☐ | ☐ | ☐ |
| Helpful if someone is hurt, upset or feeling ill | ☐ | ☐ | ☐ |
| Constantly fidgeting or squirming | ☐ | ☐ | ☐ |
| Has at least one good friend | ☐ | ☐ | ☐ |
| Often fights with other children or bullies them | ☐ | ☐ | ☐ |
| Often unhappy, downhearted or tearful | ☐ | ☐ | ☐ |
| Generally liked by other children | ☐ | ☐ | ☐ |
| Easily distracted, concentration wanders | ☐ | ☐ | ☐ |
| Nervous or clingy in new situations, easily loses confidence | ☐ | ☐ | ☐ |
| Kind to younger children | ☐ | ☐ | ☐ |
| Often argumentative with adults | ☐ | ☐ | ☐ |
| Picked on or bullied by other children | ☐ | ☐ | ☐ |
| Often volunteers to help others (parents, teachers, other children) | ☐ | ☐ | ☐ |
| Can stop and think things over before acting | ☐ | ☐ | ☐ |
| Can be spiteful to others | ☐ | ☐ | ☐ |
| Gets on better with adults than with other children | ☐ | ☐ | ☐ |
| Many fears, easily scared | ☐ | ☐ | ☐ |
| Sees tasks through to the end, good attention span | ☐ | ☐ | ☐ |

**Please complete questions on the next page…**

10

**Overall, do you think that your child has difficulties in one or more of the following areas: emotions, concentration, behaviour or being able to get on with other people?**

| No difficulties | Yes – minor difficulties | Yes – more serious difficulties | Yes – severe difficulties |
|---|---|---|---|
| ☐ | ☐ | ☐ | ☐ |

If you have answered **'Yes'**, please answer the following questions about these difficulties:

• How long have these difficulties been present?

| Less than a month | 1–5 months | 5–12 months | Over a year |
|---|---|---|---|
| ☐ | ☐ | ☐ | ☐ |

• Do the difficulties upset or distress your child?

| Not at all | Only a little | Quite a lot | A great deal |
|---|---|---|---|
| ☐ | ☐ | ☐ | ☐ |

• Do the difficulties interfere with your child's everyday life in the following areas?

| | Not at all | Only a little | Quite a lot | A great deal |
|---|---|---|---|---|
| Home life | ☐ | ☐ | ☐ | ☐ |
| Friendships | ☐ | ☐ | ☐ | ☐ |
| Learning | ☐ | ☐ | ☐ | ☐ |
| Leisure activities | ☐ | ☐ | ☐ | ☐ |

• Do the difficulties put a burden on you or the family as a whole?

| Not at all | Only a little | Quite a lot | A great deal |
|---|---|---|---|
| ☐ | ☐ | ☐ | ☐ |

Signature _____

Date _____

Mother/Father/Other (please specify) _____

**Thank you very much for your help**

# Strengths and Difficulties
## QUESTIONNAIRE

## TO BE COMPLETED BY A MAIN CARER OF A CHILD AGED BETWEEN 4 AND 16

For each item, please mark the box for Not True, Somewhat True or Certainly True. It would help us if you answered all items as best you can even if you are not absolutely certain, or the items seem daft! Please give your answers on the basis of the child's behaviour over the last six months.

Child's Name _____  Male/Female  Date of Birth _____

| | Not True | Somewhat True | Certainly True |
|---|---|---|---|
| Considerate of other people's feelings | ☐ | ☐ | ☐ |
| Restless, overactive, cannot sit still for long | ☐ | ☐ | ☐ |
| Often complains of headaches, stomach-aches or sickness | ☐ | ☐ | ☐ |
| Shares readily with other children (treats, toys, pencils etc.) | ☐ | ☐ | ☐ |
| Often has temper tantrums or hot tempers | ☐ | ☐ | ☐ |
| Rather solitary, tends to play alone | ☐ | ☐ | ☐ |
| Generally obedient, usually does what adults request | ☐ | ☐ | ☐ |
| Many worries, often seems worried | ☐ | ☐ | ☐ |
| Helpful if someone is hurt, upset or feeling ill | ☐ | ☐ | ☐ |
| Constantly fidgeting or squirming | ☐ | ☐ | ☐ |
| Has at least one good friend | ☐ | ☐ | ☐ |
| Often fights with other children or bullies them | ☐ | ☐ | ☐ |
| Often unhappy, downhearted or tearful | ☐ | ☐ | ☐ |
| Generally liked by other children | ☐ | ☐ | ☐ |
| Easily distracted, concentration wanders | ☐ | ☐ | ☐ |
| Nervous or clingy in new situations, easily loses confidence | ☐ | ☐ | ☐ |
| Kind to younger children | ☐ | ☐ | ☐ |
| Often lies or cheats | ☐ | ☐ | ☐ |
| Picked on or bullied by other children | ☐ | ☐ | ☐ |
| Often volunteers to help others (parents, teachers, other children) | ☐ | ☐ | ☐ |
| Thinks things out before acting | ☐ | ☐ | ☐ |
| Steals from home, school or elsewhere | ☐ | ☐ | ☐ |
| Gets on better with adults than with other children | ☐ | ☐ | ☐ |
| Many fears, easily scared | ☐ | ☐ | ☐ |
| Sees tasks through to the end, good attention span | ☐ | ☐ | ☐ |

**Please complete questions on the next page…**

**Overall, do you think that your child has difficulties in one or more of the following areas: emotions, concentration, behaviour or being able to get on with other people?**

| No difficulties | Yes – minor difficulties | Yes – more serious difficulties | Yes – severe difficulties |
|---|---|---|---|
| ☐ | ☐ | ☐ | ☐ |

If you have answered '**Yes**', please answer the following questions about these difficulties:

• How long have these difficulties been present?

| Less than a month | 1–5 months | 5–12 months | Over a year |
|---|---|---|---|
| ☐ | ☐ | ☐ | ☐ |

• Do the difficulties upset or distress your child?

| Not at all | Only a little | Quite a lot | A great deal |
|---|---|---|---|
| ☐ | ☐ | ☐ | ☐ |

• Do the difficulties interfere with your child's everyday life in the following areas?

| | Not at all | Only a little | Quite a lot | A great deal |
|---|---|---|---|---|
| Home life | ☐ | ☐ | ☐ | ☐ |
| Friendships | ☐ | ☐ | ☐ | ☐ |
| Classroom Learning | ☐ | ☐ | ☐ | ☐ |
| Leisure activities | ☐ | ☐ | ☐ | ☐ |

• Do the difficulties put a burden on you or the family as a whole?

| Not at all | Only a little | Quite a lot | A great deal |
|---|---|---|---|
| ☐ | ☐ | ☐ | ☐ |

Signature _____

Date _____

Mother/Father/Other (please specify) _____

**Thank you very much for your help**

# Strengths and Difficulties
## QUESTIONNAIRE

## TO BE COMPLETED BY A YOUNG PERSON BETWEEN 11 AND 16

Please read the questionnaire carefully. For each of the statements put a tick in the box that **you** think is most like you. It would help us if you put a tick for all the statements – even if it seems a bit daft! Please give answers on the basis of how you have been feeling over the last six months.

Your Name _____ Male/Female     Date of Birth _____

| | Not True | Somewhat True | Certainly True |
|---|---|---|---|
| I try to be nice to people. I care about their feelings | ☐ | ☐ | ☐ |
| I get restless, I cannot sit still for long | ☐ | ☐ | ☐ |
| I get a lot of headaches, stomach-aches or sickness | ☐ | ☐ | ☐ |
| I usually share with others (food, games, pens etc.) | ☐ | ☐ | ☐ |
| I get very angry and often lose my temper | ☐ | ☐ | ☐ |
| I am usually on my own. I generally play alone or keep to myself | ☐ | ☐ | ☐ |
| I usually do as I am told | ☐ | ☐ | ☐ |
| I worry a lot | ☐ | ☐ | ☐ |
| I am helpful if someone is hurt, upset or feeling ill | ☐ | ☐ | ☐ |
| I am constantly fidgeting or squirming | ☐ | ☐ | ☐ |
| I have one good friend or more | ☐ | ☐ | ☐ |
| I fight a lot. I can make other people do what I want | ☐ | ☐ | ☐ |
| I am often unhappy, downhearted or tearful | ☐ | ☐ | ☐ |
| Other people my age generally like me | ☐ | ☐ | ☐ |
| I am easily distracted, I find it difficult to concentrate | ☐ | ☐ | ☐ |
| I am nervous in new situations. I easily lose confidence | ☐ | ☐ | ☐ |
| I am kind to younger children | ☐ | ☐ | ☐ |
| I am often accused of cheating or lying | ☐ | ☐ | ☐ |
| Other children or young people pick on or bully me | ☐ | ☐ | ☐ |
| I often volunteer to help others (parents, teachers, children) | ☐ | ☐ | ☐ |
| I think before I do things | ☐ | ☐ | ☐ |
| I take things that are not mine from home, school or elsewhere | ☐ | ☐ | ☐ |
| I get on better with adults than with people my own age | ☐ | ☐ | ☐ |
| I have many fears, I am easily scared | ☐ | ☐ | ☐ |
| I finish the things I'm doing. My attention is good | ☐ | ☐ | ☐ |

**Please complete questions on the next page…**

14

**Overall, do you think that you have difficulties in one or more of the following areas: emotions, concentration, behaviour or being able to get on with other people?**

| No difficulties | Yes – minor difficulties | Yes – more serious difficulties | Yes – very severe difficulties |
|:---:|:---:|:---:|:---:|
| ☐ | ☐ | ☐ | ☐ |

If you have answered '**Yes**', please answer the following questions about these difficulties:

- How long have these difficulties been present?

| Less than a month | 1–5 months | 5–12 months | Over a year |
|:---:|:---:|:---:|:---:|
| ☐ | ☐ | ☐ | ☐ |

- Do the difficulties upset or distress you?

| Not at all | Only a little | Quite a lot | A great deal |
|:---:|:---:|:---:|:---:|
| ☐ | ☐ | ☐ | ☐ |

- Do the difficulties interfere with your everyday life in the following areas?

| | Not at all | Only a little | Quite a lot | A great deal |
|---|:---:|:---:|:---:|:---:|
| Home life | ☐ | ☐ | ☐ | ☐ |
| Friendships | ☐ | ☐ | ☐ | ☐ |
| Classroom Learning | ☐ | ☐ | ☐ | ☐ |
| Leisure activities | ☐ | ☐ | ☐ | ☐ |

- Do the difficulties make it harder for those around you (family, friends, teachers etc.)?

| Not at all | Only a little | Quite a lot | A great deal |
|:---:|:---:|:---:|:---:|
| ☐ | ☐ | ☐ | ☐ |

Signature _____

Date _____

**Thank you very much for your help**

# GUIDANCE ON USING STRENGTHS AND DIFFICULTIES QUESTIONNAIRES

## Background

1. Evaluation of children's emotional and behavioural development is a central component of social work assessment.

2. These questionnaires screen for child emotional and behavioural problems. These scales are similar to older scales such as Rutter A & B Scales developed for use by parents and teachers, but put a greater emphasis on strengths.

## The Scales

3. The questionnaires consist of 25 items that refer to different emotions or behaviours.

4. For each item the respondent marks in one of three boxes to indicate whether the item is **not** true, **somewhat** true or **certainly** true for the child in question.

5. On the back of each questionnaire are questions that aim to address severity by scoring duration of the difficulties and their impact on the child, themselves or others.

6. Children's emotional and behavioural problems are not always evident in all situations. When they are, the problem is usually more severe. As with the Rutter scales, the Strengths and Difficulties Questionnaires have both parent and teacher versions.

7. In young children, parents' reports of their emotions and behaviour are usually more reliable than those of the children themselves, but in adolescence, parents are often unaware of their children's emotional state. There is therefore a Strengths and Difficulties questionnaire for young people aged 11–16.

8. The Rutter scales were originally devised for children aged 9–10, and have been shown to be valid for those aged 6–16. The Strengths and Difficulties Scale covers ages 4–16, and there is an additional scale for children aged 3–4.

9. The scales can be scored to produce an overall score that indicates whether the child/young person is likely to have a significant problem. Selected items can also be used to form subscales for Pro-social Behaviour, Hyperactivity, Emotional Symptoms, Conduct and Peer problems.

## Use

10. The questionnaires are of value in both assessments and for evaluating progress.

11. They can give an indication of whether a child/young person is likely to have a significant emotional or behavioural problem/disorder, and what type of disorder it is.

12. During piloting, over half the children assessed scored above the cut-off scores indicating a probable disorder.

13. The most common problems were Hyperactivity, Peer and Conduct problems. These were identified in over half the children.

14. One social worker commented that the questionnaire 'gave a more in-depth look at the young person'. Another said that with the individual child/young person it could be a springboard for therapeutic action, and that it would be helpful, alongside work with the family, to monitor progress.

## Administration

15. The respondent – whether parent, child or teacher – needs to understand where the use of the questionnaire fits into the overall assessment.

16. It is usually best if the respondent completes the questionnaire in the presence of the social worker. Sometimes it will be necessary for the worker to administer the scale verbally.

17. The scale takes about 10 minutes to complete.

18. It is preferable if full discussion is kept to the end, but there will be occasions when what the respondent says while completing the scale should be acknowledged immediately.

19. Fuller discussion is vital for several reasons. Firstly, it is important to establish level and nature of any difficulties more clearly. Information from other sources is also relevant for this purpose. Secondly, the overall score may be below the cut off point indicative of disorder, but there may still be issues that are important to the respondent. The response to a single item might provide the cue. Thirdly, it is crucial to understand how the child, parent and other family members are responding to how the child is, or what the child is doing/saying.

## Scoring

20. This is explained on the sheet that accompanies the questionnaires.

21. Each item is scored 0, 1 or 2. Somewhat true is always scored 1, but whether Not true and Certainly true are scored 0 or 2 depends on whether the item is framed as a strength or difficulty.

22. The scoring sheet explains which item contributes to which subscales. The Pro-social scale is scored so that an absence of pro-social behaviour scores low. A child may have difficulties but if they have a high Pro-social score the outlook for intervention is better.

23. The scoring sheet has a chart, which indicates which total scores are low, average or high in the general population. High scores overall or for any subscale point to the likelihood of a significant disorder, and/or a disorder of a particular type. They do not guarantee that there will be found to be a disorder when a more thorough assessment is conducted. Neither does a low score guarantee the absence of a problem, but the instrument is useful for screening.

## References

Goodman R (1997). The Strengths and Difficulties Questionnaire: A reseach note. *Journal of Child Psychology and Psychiatry*. **38**: 581–586.

Goodman R, Meltzer H and Bailey V (1998) The strengths and difficulties questionnaire: A pilot study on the validity of the self-report version. *European Child & Adolescent Psychiatry*. **7**: 125–130.

## SCORING THE SELF REPORT STRENGTHS AND DIFFICULTIES QUESTIONNAIRE

The 25 items in the SDQ comprise 5 scales of 5 items each. The first stage of scoring the questionnaire is generally to score each of the 5 scales. Somewhat true is always scored as 1, but the scoring of Not True and Certainly True varies with each item. The score for each response category is given below scale by scale.

### Pro-social Scale

|  | NOT TRUE | SOMEWHAT TRUE | CERTAINLY TRUE |
| --- | --- | --- | --- |
| I am considerate of others | 0 | 1 | 2 |
| I usually share | 0 | 1 | 2 |
| I am helpful if | 0 | 1 | 2 |
| I am kinder to younger | 0 | 1 | 2 |
| I often volunteer | 0 | 1 | 2 |

### Hyperactivity Scale

|  | NOT TRUE | SOMEWHAT TRUE | CERTAINLY TRUE |
| --- | --- | --- | --- |
| I am restless | 0 | 1 | 2 |
| I am constantly fidgeting | 0 | 1 | 2 |
| I am easily distracted | 0 | 1 | 2 |
| Thinks things out | 2 | 1 | 0 |
| I see tasks through | 2 | 1 | 0 |

## Emotional Symptoms Scale

|  | NOT TRUE | SOMEWHAT TRUE | CERTAINLY TRUE |
|---|---|---|---|
| I get a lot of headaches | 0 | 1 | 2 |
| I worry a lot | 0 | 1 | 2 |
| I am often unhappy | 0 | 1 | 2 |
| I am nervous in | 0 | 1 | 2 |
| I have many fears | 0 | 1 | 2 |

## Conduct Problems Scale

|  | NOT TRUE | SOMEWHAT TRUE | CERTAINLY TRUE |
|---|---|---|---|
| I get very angry | 0 | 1 | 2 |
| I usually do as I am told | 2 | 1 | 0 |
| I fight a lot | 0 | 1 | 2 |
| I am often accused of lying | 0 | 1 | 2 |
| I take things | 0 | 1 | 2 |

## Peer Problems Scale

|  | NOT TRUE | SOMEWHAT TRUE | CERTAINLY TRUE |
|---|---|---|---|
| I am rather solitary | 0 | 1 | 2 |
| I have at least one good friend | 2 | 1 | 0 |
| Other people … like me | 2 | 1 | 0 |
| Other … people pick on me … | 0 | 1 | 2 |
| I get on better with adults … | 0 | 1 | 2 |

For each of the 5 scales the score can range from 0 to 10 provided all five items have been completed. You can prorate the scores if there are only one or two missing items.

To generate a total difficulties score, sum the four scales dealing with problems but do not include the pro-social scale. The resultant score can range from 0 to 40. Provided at least 12 of the relevant 20 items are completed, you can prorate the total if necessary.

## Interpreting scores and identifying need

The provisional bandings shown below have been selected so that roughly 80% of children in the community do not have needs in these areas, 10% have some needs, and 10% have high needs.

## Self completed

|  | LOW NEED | SOME NEED | HIGH NEED |
|---|---|---|---|
| Total difficulties score | 0–15 | 16–19 | 20–40 |
| Conduct problems score | 0–3 | 4 | 5–10 |
| Hyperactivity score | 0–5 | 6 | 7–10 |
| Emotional symptoms score | 0–5 | 6 | 7–10 |
| Peer problem score | 0–3 | 4–5 | 6–10 |
| Pro-social behaviour score | 6–10 | 5 | 0–4 |

# Parenting Daily Hassles

SCALES

# Parenting Daily Hassles
## SCALE

The statements below describe a lot of events that routinely occur in families with young children. These events sometimes make life difficult. Please read each item and circle how often it happens to you (rarely, sometimes, a lot, or constantly) and then circle how much of a 'hassle' you feel that it has been for you **FOR THE PAST 6 MONTHS**. If you have more than one child, these events can include any or all of your children.

| EVENT | How often it happens | | | | Hassle (low to high) | | | | |
|---|---|---|---|---|---|---|---|---|---|
| 1. Continually cleaning up messes of toys or food | Rarely | Sometimes | A lot | Constantly | 1 | 2 | 3 | 4 | 5 |
| 2. Being nagged, whined at, complained to | Rarely | Sometimes | A lot | Constantly | 1 | 2 | 3 | 4 | 5 |
| 3. Meal-time difficulties with picky eaters, complaining etc. | Rarely | Sometimes | A lot | Constantly | 1 | 2 | 3 | 4 | 5 |
| 4. The kids won't listen or do what they are asked without being nagged | Rarely | Sometimes | A lot | Constantly | 1 | 2 | 3 | 4 | 5 |
| 5. Baby-sitters are hard to find | Rarely | Sometimes | A lot | Constantly | 1 | 2 | 3 | 4 | 5 |
| 6. The kids schedules (like pre-school or other activities) interfere with meeting your own household needs | Rarely | Sometimes | A lot | Constantly | 1 | 2 | 3 | 4 | 5 |
| 7. Sibling arguments or fights require a 'referee' | Rarely | Sometimes | A lot | Constantly | 1 | 2 | 3 | 4 | 5 |
| 8. The kids demand that you entertain them or play with them | Rarely | Sometimes | A lot | Constantly | 1 | 2 | 3 | 4 | 5 |
| 9. The kids resist or struggle with you over bed-time | Rarely | Sometimes | A lot | Constantly | 1 | 2 | 3 | 4 | 5 |
| 10. The kids are constantly underfoot, interfering with other chores | Rarely | Sometimes | A lot | Constantly | 1 | 2 | 3 | 4 | 5 |
| 11. The need to keep a constant eye on where the kids are and what they are doing | Rarely | Sometimes | A lot | Constantly | 1 | 2 | 3 | 4 | 5 |
| 12. The kids interrupt adult conversations or interactions | Rarely | Sometimes | A lot | Constantly | 1 | 2 | 3 | 4 | 5 |
| 13. Having to change your plans because of unprecedented child needs | Rarely | Sometimes | A lot | Constantly | 1 | 2 | 3 | 4 | 5 |
| 14. The kids get dirty several times a day requiring changes of clothing | Rarely | Sometimes | A lot | Constantly | 1 | 2 | 3 | 4 | 5 |
| 15. Difficulties in getting privacy (eg. in the bathroom) | Rarely | Sometimes | A lot | Constantly | 1 | 2 | 3 | 4 | 5 |
| 16. The kids are hard to manage in public (grocery store, shopping centre, restaurant) | Rarely | Sometimes | A lot | Constantly | 1 | 2 | 3 | 4 | 5 |
| 17. Difficulties in getting kids ready for outings and leaving on time | Rarely | Sometimes | A lot | Constantly | 1 | 2 | 3 | 4 | 5 |
| 18. Difficulties in leaving kids for a night out or at school or day care | Rarely | Sometimes | A lot | Constantly | 1 | 2 | 3 | 4 | 5 |
| 19. The kids have difficulties with friends (eg. fighting, trouble, getting along, or no friends available) | Rarely | Sometimes | A lot | Constantly | 1 | 2 | 3 | 4 | 5 |
| 20. Having to run extra errands to meet the kids needs | Rarely | Sometimes | A lot | Constantly | 1 | 2 | 3 | 4 | 5 |

Questionnaire completed by *mother/father/adoptive parent/foster carer* (please specify)

# GUIDANCE ON USING PARENTING DAILY HASSLES SCALE

## Background

1. This scale aims to assess the frequency and intensity/impact of 20 experiences that can be a 'hassle' to parents.

2. It has been used in a wide variety of research concerned with children and families. The research in which it has been used includes a parenting programme with families who had major difficulties in raising young children.

3. Parents/Caregivers enjoy completing the scale, because it touches on aspects of being a parent that are very familiar. It helps them express what it feels like to be a parent.

4. During piloting, social workers reported that it depicted concisely areas of pressure felt by the carer. This helped identify areas where assistance could be provided either by the social services department or other agencies.

5. It is seen by parents as a way for them to express their needs for help with parenting.

## The Scale

6. The caregiver is asked to score each of the 20 potential **Hassles** in two different ways for frequency and intensity.

7. The frequency of each type of happening provides an 'objective' marker of how often it occurs.

8. The intensity or impact score indicates the caregiver's 'subjective' appraisal of how much those events affect or 'hassle' them.

9. The time frame for this scale can be varied according to the focus of the assessment. For example, if a family is thought to have been under particular pressure in the last 2 months the parent can be asked to consider how matters have been during that period. However, if it is intended to assess progress, the same time frame should be used on each occasion. Periods of less than one month are probably too short to give a useful picture.

## Use

10. The caregiver should understand the aim of filling out the questionnaire, and how it will contribute to the overall assessment.

11. The scale is probably most useful with families that are not well-known. In piloting it was found to highlight areas for future discussion, and help prioritise which parenting issues should be addressed first.

12. It can also be used to monitor change.

## Administration

13. It should be given to the parent/caregiver to fill out themselves.

14. It can be read out if necessary.

15. It takes about 10 minutes to complete.

16. The scale should always be used as a basis for discussion. In general this is best kept until the parent has finished, but there will be occasions when it is vital to acknowledge, or immediately follow up comments made while it is being filled out.

## Scoring

17. The scale can be used in two distinct ways: (a) the totals of the frequency and intensity scales can be obtained, or (b) scores for challenging behaviour and parenting tasks can be derived from the intensity scale.

18. To obtain frequency and intensity total scores

    (a) The frequency scale is scored: rarely = 1, sometimes = 2, a lot = 3, and constantly = 4. If the parent says that an event never occurs, never = 0.

The range for this scale is 0–80. A score of 3 or 4 for any one event indicates that it occurs with above average frequency.

(b) The intensity scale is scored by adding the parents rating of 1–5 for each item. If a 0 has been scored for frequency on an item then it should be scored 0 for intensity. The range for this scale is 0–100. A score of 4 or 5 for any one event indicates that it is at least some problem to the parent.

## Scoring

19. (a) The challenging behaviour total score is obtained by adding the intensity scale scores for items: 2, 4, 8, 9, 11, 12, 16. Range: 0–35.

    (b) The parenting tasks total score is obtained by adding the intensity scale scores for items: 1, 6, 7, 10, 13, 14, 17, 20. Range: 0–40.

20. There is no cut off for any of the scales but total scores above 50 on the frequency scale or above 70 on the intensity scale indicate on the one hand a high frequency of potentially hassling happenings, and on the other that the parent is experiencing significant pressure over parenting.

21. Events occurring with frequency 3 or 4, or intensity 4 or 5, particularly those where the parent rates high intensity or impact, should be discussed to clarify the extent of need.

22. The total score on the challenging behaviour and parenting tasks scales may be useful in indicating how the parent/caregiver sees the situation, whether difficulties lie in the troublesome behaviour of the children, or the burden of meeting the 'expected' or 'legitimate' needs of the children. The subscores may also be useful in monitoring change.

## References

Crnic KA & Greenberg MT (1990) Minor parenting stresses with young children. *Child Development.* **61**: 1628–1637

Crnic KA & Booth CL (1991) Mothers' and fathers' perceptions of daily hassles of parenting across early childhood. *Journal of Marriage and the Family.* **53**: 1043–1050.

# Home Conditions

ASSESSMENT

DH Department of Health

# GUIDANCE ON USING HOME CONDITIONS ASSESSMENT

## Background

1. Social workers assess physical aspects of the home environment.

2. This scale may appear judgmental, but workers necessarily make judgements about the safety, order and cleanliness of the place in which the child lives. The use of a list helps the objectivity of observation.

3. The total score has been found to correlate highly with children's abilities, so that children from homes with low scores usually have better language and intellectual development. This does not mean that all children from high scoring homes will have poor intellectual progress.

4. Like all methods of assessment it should not be used in isolation – other sources of information, including the quality of the parent-child relationship will contribute to the overall assessment.

## The Scale

5. The assessment is identical to the Family Cleanliness Scale devised by Davie and others (1984).

6. This is a list of 11 items to be observed during home visits.

7. Social presentation, namely the cleanliness of the children is included.

## Use

8. The scale if best used as a mental checklist to provide a framework for observation.

9. It is particularly appropriate to use during initial assessment. Once used it is a method of keeping track of progress or deterioration.

10. In order to be able to complete the scale it is necessary to look over the home. The caregiver can be asked whether they have any problems with their housing, or whether the nature of their accommodation causes difficulties from the point of view of brining up the children. This can lead naturally to a request to look round.

11. It will usually be unhelpful to share all that has been observed with the caregiver. This could upset the establishment of partnership – a good working relationship is of overriding importance. However the worker needs to have a clear picture of the environment from the child's point of view.

12. Individual items can be a focus for a piece of work. This might be to encourage the parent to attend to something that could pose a health risk to the children, or to bring in additional support where the parent is unlikely to be able to improve matters unassisted.

## Scoring

13. The scoring is binary 0 if the condition is not present, and 1 if it is.

14. Items are scored on the basis of what is observed. Why the conditions are as they are is not taken into account. Of course the worker needs to understand why matters are as they are to take appropriate action. The scale charts the child environment as it is.

15. The scale has no cut off. Depending on the age of the children different items may give more or less concern, but in general the higher the score the greater the concern.

16. Individual items may require action whatever the total score.

## Reference

Davie CE, Hutt SJ, Vincent E & Mason M (1984) *The young child at home.* NFER-Nelson, Windsor

## THE SCALE

| | | | |
|---|---|---|---|
| 1. | Smell (e.g. stale cigarette smoke, rotting food) | 0 | 1 |
| 2. | Kitchen floor soiled, covered in bits, crumbs etc. | 0 | 1 |
| 3. | Floor covering in any other room soiled as above. | 0 | 1 |
| 4. | General decorative order poor – obviously in need of attention (e.g. badly stained wall paper, broken windows) | 0 | 1 |

| | | |
|---|---|---|
| 5. Kitchen sink, draining board, work surfaces or cupboard door have not been washed for a considerable period of time | 0 | 1 |
| 6. Other surfaces in the house have not been dusted for a considerable period of time | 0 | 1 |
| 7. Cooking implements, cutlery or crockery showing ingrained dirt and or these items remain unwashed until they are needed again. | 0 | 1 |
| 8. Lavatory, bath or basin showing ingrained dirt. | 0 | 1 |
| 9. Furnishings or furniture soiled | 0 | 1 |
| 10. Informant's or children's, clothing clearly unwashed, or hair matted and unbrushed | 0 | 1 |
| 11. Garden or yard uncared for and strewn with rubbish | 0 | 1 |

**Total Score** _____

# Adult
# Wellbeing

SCALE

# ADULT WELLBEING SCALE

This form has been designed so that you can show how you have been feeling in the past few days.

Read each item in turn and UNDERLINE the response which shows best how you are feeling or have been feeling in the last few days.

Please complete all of the questionnaire.

1.   **I feel cheerful**

   Yes, definitely          Yes, sometimes          No, not much          No, not at all

2.   **I can sit down and relax quite easily**

   Yes, definitely          Yes, sometimes          No, not much          No, not at all

3.   **My appetite is**

   Very poor          Fairly poor          Quite good          Very good

4.   **I lose my temper and shout and snap at others**

   Yes, definitely          Yes, sometimes          No, not much          No, not at all

5.   **I can laugh and feel amused**

   Yes, definitely          Yes, sometimes          No, not much          No, not at all

6.   **I feel I might lose control and hit or hurt someone**

   Sometimes          Occasionally          Rarely          Never

7.   **I have an uncomfortable feeling like butterflies in the stomach**

   Yes, definitely          Yes, sometimes          Not very often          Not at all

8.   **The thought of hurting myself occurs to me**

   Sometimes          Not very often          Hardly ever          Not at all

9.   **I'm awake before I need to get up**

   For 2 hours          For about 1 hour          For less than          Not at all. I
   or more                                        1 hour                sleep until it is
                                                                        time to get up

10.   **I feel tense or 'wound up'**

   Yes, definitely          Yes, sometimes          No, not much          No, not at all

11. **I feel like harming myself**

| | | | |
|---|---|---|---|
| Yes, definitely | Yes, sometimes | No, not much | No, not at all |

12. **I've kept up my old interests**

| | | | |
|---|---|---|---|
| Yes, most of them | Yes, some of them | No, not many of them | No, none of them |

13. **I am patient with other people**

| | | | |
|---|---|---|---|
| All the time | Most of the time | Some of the time | Hardly ever |

14. **I get scared or panicky for no very good reason**

| | | | |
|---|---|---|---|
| Yes, definitely | Yes, sometimes | No, not much | No, not at all |

15. **I get angry with myself or call myself names**

| | | | |
|---|---|---|---|
| Yes, definitely | Yes, sometimes | Not often | No, not at all |

16. **People upset me so that I feel like slamming doors or banging about**

| | | | |
|---|---|---|---|
| Yes, often | Yes, sometimes | Only occasionally | Not at all |

17. **I can go out on my own without feeling anxious**

| | | | |
|---|---|---|---|
| Yes, always | Yes, sometimes | No, not often | No, I never can |

18. **Lately I have been getting annoyed with myself**

| | | | |
|---|---|---|---|
| Very much so | Rather a lot | Not much | Not at all |

# GUIDANCE ON USING ADULT WELLBEING SCALE

## Background

1. Parent/Caregiver mental health is a fundamental component of assessment.

2. There is evidence that some people respond more openly to a questionnaire than a face to face interview, when reporting on their mental health.

3. A questionnaire gives caregivers the opportunity to express themselves without having to face another person, however sympathetic that person may be.

4. A questionnaire is no substitute for a good relationship, but it can contribute to the development of a rapport if discussed sensitively.

5. During piloting the use of the questionnaire was found to convey the social worker's concern for the parent's wellbeing. This can be particularly valuable where the parent feels their needs are not being considered.

## The Scale

6. The scale is the Irritability, Depression, Anxiety (IDA) Scale developed by Snaith *et al* (1978).

7. This scale allows respondents four possible responses to each item.

8. Four aspects of wellbeing are covered: Depression, Anxiety and Inwardly and Outwardly directed Irritability.

## Use

9. In principle the questionnaire can be used with any adult, who is in contact with the child whose development and context are being assessed. In practice this will usually be the main caregiver(s).

10. In piloting social workers reported that use of the scale raised issues on more than half the occasions that it was used. Probable depression was found amongst almost half the caregivers, and significant anxiety in a third.

11. Where social workers were new to the family situation they said they learnt things they did not know. 'It helped me to be aware of the carers' needs', and 'highlighted stresses'. It helped focus on 'parents' needs and feelings'.

12. Even when parents were known to the workers it gave topics an airing and clarified areas to work on; it 'released tension'.

13. Progress can also be registered. It was 'useful to measure when things were calmer'.

14. Used flexibly it can provide openings to discuss many areas including feelings about relationships with partners and children.

## Administration

15. It is vital that the respondent understands why they are being asked to complete the scale. Some will be concerned that revealing mental health needs will prejudice their chances of continuing to care for their child. For example, it can be explained that many carers of children experience considerable stress, and it is important to understand this if they are to be given appropriate support.

16. The scale is best filled out by the carer themselves in the presence of the worker, but it can be administered verbally.

17. It takes about 10 minutes to complete.

18. **Discussion is essential**. Usually this will be when the questionnaire has been completed, so the respondent has an opportunity to consider their own needs uninterrupted. However, there will be times when an important clue to how the caregiver feels may be best picked up immediately. One example occurred during piloting, when a respondent expressed distaste for questions about self-harm.

## Scoring

19. The sheet accompanying the questionnaire indicates the method of scoring the 4 subscales.

20. Use of cut-off scores gives indicators of significant care needs with respect to depression, anxiety, and inwardly and outwardly directed irritability. Inward irritability can point to the possibility of self-harm. Outward irritability raises the possibility of angry actions towards the child(ren).

21. As with any screening instrument, interpretation must be in the context of other information. Some respondents will underreport distress, others exaggerate it. A high or low score on any scale does not guarantee that a significant level of need is present.

22. Most value is obtained by using the scale as a springboard for discussion.

## Reference

Snaith RP, Constantopoulos AA, Jardine MY & McGuffin P (1978) A clinical scale for the self-assessment of irritability. British Journal of Psychiatry 132: 163–71.

## SCORING THE ADULT WELLBEING SCALE

1. Depression – Questions 1,3,5,9 and 12 look at depression. The possible response scores that are shown below run from the left to the right – i.e. for question 1 'I feel cheerful', the scores would be looked at from 'yes, definitely' (0), 'yes, sometimes' (1), 'no, not much' (2), 'no, not at all' (3)
   A score of 4–6 is borderline in this scale and a score above this may indicate a problem.

| QU1 | QU3 | QU5 | QU9 | QU12 |
|---|---|---|---|---|
| 0,1,2,3 | 3,2,1,0 | 0,1,2,3 | 3,2,1,0 | 0,1,2,3 |

2. Anxiety – Questions 2,7,10,14 and 17 look at anxiety. A score of 6–8 is borderline, above this level may indicate a problem in this area.

| QU2 | QU7 | QU10 | QU14 | QU17 |
|---|---|---|---|---|
| 0,1,2,3 | 3,2,1,0 | 3,2,1,0 | 3,2,1,0 | 0,1,2,3 |

3. Outward directed irritability – Questions 4,6,13 and 16 look at outward directed irritability. A score of 5–7 is borderline for this scale, and a score above this may indicate a problem in this area.

| QU4 | QU6 | QU13 | QU16 |
|---|---|---|---|
| 3,2,1,0 | 3,2,1,0 | 0,1,2,3 | 3,2,1,0 |

4. Inward directed irritability – Questions 8,11,15 and 18 look at inward directed irritability. A score of 4–6 is borderline, a higher score may indicate a problem.

| QU8 | QU11 | QU15 | QU18 |
|---|---|---|---|
| 3,2,1,0 | 3,2,1,0 | 3,2,1,0 | 3,2,1,0 |

Use of cut-off scores gives indicators of significant care needs with respect to depression, anxiety, and inwardly and outwardly directed irritability. Inward irritability can point to the possibility of selfharm. Outward irritability raises the possibility of angry actions towards the child(ren).

As with any screening instrument, interpretation must be in the context of other information. Some respondents will underreport distress, others exaggerate. A high or low score on any scale does not guarantee that significant level of need is present.

Most value is obtained by using the scale as a springboard for discussion.

# Adolescent Wellbeing

SCALE

# Adolescent Wellbeing

## SCALE FOR YOUNG PEOPLE AGED 11 TO 16

*Please tick as appropriate*

| | Most of the time | sometimes | never |
|---|---|---|---|
| 1.  I look forward to things as much as I used to | ☐ | ☐ | ☐ |
| 2.  I sleep very well | ☐ | ☐ | ☐ |
| 3.  I feel like crying | ☐ | ☐ | ☐ |
| 4.  I like going out | ☐ | ☐ | ☐ |
| 5.  I feel like leaving home | ☐ | ☐ | ☐ |
| 6.  I get stomache-aches/cramps | ☐ | ☐ | ☐ |
| 7.  I have lots of energy | ☐ | ☐ | ☐ |
| 8.  I enjoy my food | ☐ | ☐ | ☐ |
| 9.  I can stick up for myself | ☐ | ☐ | ☐ |
| 10.  I think life isn't worth living | ☐ | ☐ | ☐ |
| 11.  I am good at things I do | ☐ | ☐ | ☐ |
| 12.  I enjoy the things I do as much as I used to | ☐ | ☐ | ☐ |
| 13.  I like talking to my friends and family | ☐ | ☐ | ☐ |
| 14.  I have horrible dreams | ☐ | ☐ | ☐ |
| 15.  I feel very lonely | ☐ | ☐ | ☐ |
| 16.  I am easily cheered up | ☐ | ☐ | ☐ |
| 17.  I feel so sad I can hardly bear it | ☐ | ☐ | ☐ |
| 18.  I feel very bored | ☐ | ☐ | ☐ |

# GUIDANCE ON USING ADOLESCENT WELLBEING SCALE

## Background

1. How young people feel in themselves is a vital part of any assessment.

2. It is important to understand their worries and concerns, and whether they are depressed or even suicidal.

3. There is good evidence that the way a young person is feeling is often not recognised by their parents or caregivers. This makes it particularly important to have a way of helping them to express directly how they are feeling.

4. With very young children their reporting can fluctuate from day to day, or even hour to hour – they do not necessarily give a stable view of their situation. Evaluation of their perspective requires particular care, so questionnaires are not usually a good starting point

5. Older children and adolescents can give a more reliable report, which means that a questionnaire may be more helpful. As with some adults they often find it easier to respond to a questionnaire about feelings than face-to-face interviewing.

## The Scale

6. The Adolescent Wellbeing Scale was devised by Birleson to pick up possible depression in older children and adolescents. It has been shown to be effective for this purpose.

7. The scale has 18 questions – each relating to different aspects of an adolescent's life, and how they feel about these. They are asked to indicate whether the statement applies to them most of the time, sometimes or never.

8. The scale can be used by children as young as 7 or 8, but as indicated above, responses are more reliable for those aged 11 or more.

## Use

9. In piloting social workers found young people were pleased to have the opportunity to contribute to the assessment.

10. The questionnaire often helped them express their feelings. It gave 'an overall insight in a short time'. It presented a 'truer picture of the adolescent's state of mind'. 'It gave me insight into how sad and overwhelmed the young person felt'.

11. On occasions use of the scale pointed to particular issues that could be a focus for further work. It gave an opportunity for 'the young person to look at themselves'.

12. The scale has proved useful with adolescents at initial assessment, but also to monitor progress. For example, it helped 'clarify a young person's feeling about placement with their mother'.

13. During piloting over half the young people who filled out the questionnaire were above the cut-off score of 13 indicating a probable depressive disorder.

## Administration

14. The young person should understand the aim of the questionnaire, and how it fits into any wider assessment.

15. Ideally it is completed by the adolescent themselves, but, if necessary, it an be administered verbally.

16. Discussion is usually best at the end, but there may be important areas that should be picked up as the result of comments made while the questionnaire is being filled out. A number of adolescents talk as they are completing the scale, and this may provide a good opportunity to promote conversation, or establish rapport.

17. During piloting the scale took about 15 minutes to complete, ensuing discussion took longer.

## Scoring

18. The responses to each question are scored 0, 1 or 2. How the responses are scored depends on the nature of the statement that is being responded to as well as the response. 0 means that the response indicates no concern, 1 possible concern and 2 that the young person is indicating unhappiness or low self esteem with regard to that item.

    For example for question 8 – I enjoy my food – if no/never is ticked the score is 2. For question 17 – I feel so sad I can hardly bear it – a score of 2 would be obtained for most of the time.

19. A score of 13 or more has been found to indicate the likelihood of a depressive disorder. Discussion with the young person and information from other sources will be necessary to make a definite diagnosis. There will be some who score high, but who on careful consideration are not judged to have a depressive disorder, and others who score low who do have one.

20. In most instances the way a young person responds to the the different questions will be as important and as valuable as any score, because they can give an insight into that particular young person's needs. The reply to only one question may give the opportunity to understand their point of view.

## Reference

Birleson P (1980) The validity of Depressive Disorder in Childhood and the Development of a Self-Rating Scale; a Research Report. *Journal of Child Psychology and Psychiatry.* **22**: 73–88.

# Recent Life
# Events

QUESTIONNAIRE

# Recent Life Events
## QUESTIONNAIRE

Listed below are a number of events. Please read each item carefully and then indicate whether or not each event has happened to you in the past year.

Please tick the **YES** box if the event has occurred.
Please tick the **'still affects me'** box if **the event is still having an effect on your life**

| EVENT | YES | Still affects me |
|---|---|---|
| Have you had a serious illness or been seriously injured? | ☐ | ☐ |
| Has one of your immediate family * been seriously ill or injured? | ☐ | ☐ |
| Have any of your close friends or other close relatives been seriously ill or injured? | ☐ | ☐ |
| Have any of your immediate family died? | ☐ | ☐ |
| Have any of your other close relatives or close friends died? | ☐ | ☐ |
| Have you separated from your partner (not including death)? | ☐ | ☐ |
| Have you had any serious problem with a close friend, neighbour or relative? | ☐ | ☐ |
| Have you, or an immediate family member been subject to serious racial abuse, attack or /threats | ☐ | ☐ |
| Have you, or an immediate family member been subject to any abuse, attack, threat – perhaps due to you or someone close to you having a disability of any kind (i.e. a mental health problem, a learning disability or a physical problem)? | ☐ | ☐ |
| Have you, or an immediate family member been subject to any other form of serious abuse, attack, or threat? | ☐ | ☐ |
| Have you or your partner been unemployed or seeking work for more than one month? | ☐ | ☐ |
| Have you or your partner been sacked from your job or made redundant? | ☐ | ☐ |
| Have you had any major financial difficulties (e.g. debts, difficulty paying bills)? | ☐ | ☐ |
| Have you, or an immediate family member had any Police contact or been in a court appearance? | ☐ | ☐ |
| Have you or an immediate member of your family been burgled or mugged? | ☐ | ☐ |
| Have you or another individual who lives with you given birth? | ☐ | ☐ |
| Have you or another individual who lives with you suffered from a miscarriage or had a stillbirth? | ☐ | ☐ |
| Have you moved house (through choice)? | ☐ | ☐ |
| Have you moved house (not through choice)? | ☐ | ☐ |
| Have you had any housing difficulties? | ☐ | ☐ |
| Have you had any other significant event ( Please specify)? | ☐ | ☐ |

*immediate family includes: mother, father, sister, brother, partner, child*

# GUIDANCE ON USING RECENT LIFE EVENTS QUESTIONNAIRE

## Background

1. Life events are usually short-lived but may have more enduring consequences.

2. They can be distinguished from 'chronic difficulties', such as poverty or persistently discordant relationships. However life events can be both an indicator of chronic difficulties, or a precipitant of them.

3. Life events affect individuals and families in different ways, so it is important to explore how they impact on the caregivers and the family. For example, the death of a grandparent may have a practical as well as an emotional impact on the family if they have helped to support and care for the children.

4. Negative life events such as divorce, death of someone close, physical illness and unemployment have the capacity to affect any family member, not just those directly involved. Losing a parent at a young age, particularly before 11, has been reported to independently influence wellbeing in both childhood and adult life.

5. Most negative life events can be seen as involving the experience of loss, or threat of loss, including the loss of self esteem. Some apparently positive events such as job promotion may act in this way.

6. An important issue is whether an event is felt to continue to exert a negative affect. This aspect has not always been included in questionnaires.

## The Questionnaire

7. This Life Events questionnaire has been developed from one devised by Brugha et al (1985), with 9 additional items.

8. The scale aims to look at recent life events, those occurring in the last 12 months and whether the respondent thinks they have a continuing influence. However, it can be used to evaluate events and impact over a longer period if desired.

9. It can contribute to a social history, or provide an opportunity to re-evaluate whether known events are continuing to exert an influence.

## Use

10. It is expected that it will be used mostly with main caregivers, but it could be of value with potential caregivers and separated parents.

11. In piloting it was found to be 'extremely' useful in both initial assessment and continuing work. It raised new issues on three out of every four occasions on which it was used.

12. With new families the questionnaire 'gave further insight into the carer's background'. It 'put into perspective the reasons why the mother was down'.

13. With respondents with whom workers were already familiar it revealed information not previously known. It identified issues that 'the family had not considered stressful or told me'. 'It highlighted issues that were and were not still having an effect'. One social worker reported that they were able to find out the 'carer's view of issues'.

14. It is clear that social workers should be prepared for what may emerge if this instrument is used.

## Administration

15. The scale should be given to the respondent, usually a main caregiver, after appropriate preparation. This will depend on whether the context is an assessment or a review.

16. It may be helpful to acknowledge that the worker appreciates that thinking about important family events may stir up painful memories.

17. The questionnaires take about 15 minutes to complete, but discussion can take considerably longer.

18. Although not used in this way in the piloting, it could form a valuable basis for a family discussion. This would require further preparation and negotiation.

## Scoring

19.  The initial scoring is binary. 1 if the life event has happened, and 0 if it has not.

20.  The number of events that the respondent considers are still affecting them is then counted.

21.  In piloting respondents reported up to 17 events in the last year, of which up to 10 were still having an affect. The average number of events was between 7 & 8, of which about half were still considered by the caregiver to be affecting them.

22.  The questionnaire does not have a cut off point. It is scored on the basis that the more life events the adult has been through, the higher the score, and therefore the **greater** the **likelihood** of some form of longer term impact on the adult, child and or family. This will be particularly so if the person considers the events still affect them.

## Reference

Brugha T, Bebington P, Tennant C and Hurry J (1985) The list of threatening experiences: A subset of 12 life events categories with considerable long-term contextual threat. *Psychological Medicine.* **15**: 189–194.

# Family
# Activity

SCALES

# Family Activity

## SCALE FOR CHILDREN AGED 2 TO 6

Could you let me know the sort of things you do as a family, or with your child/children both regularly and in the last year. Below are some examples of activities you may have done.

If you have done any of these activities **within the timescale written in bold**, please tick in the box provided. You may also like to mention other activities you have done. You ca do this by filling in the lines at the end of this sheet.

|  | Activity if YES, please tick |
| --- | :---: |
| Have you read a story to your child **in the last week**? | ☐ |
| Has your child eaten with you and other family members at least **once in the last wee**k? | ☐ |
| Did you do anything special for your child on their **last birthday**, such as a cake, party, trip to the park etc.? | ☐ |
| Have you gone with your child/family to the park, playground, farm or similar **in the last month**? | ☐ |
| Have you gone with your child/family to a local event, such as county show, fete, **in the last 6 months**? | ☐ |
| Have you ever belonged to a mother/toddler baby group of any kind for **at least 3 months**? | ☐ |
| Have you and your child/family visited friends who have young children **in the last month**? | ☐ |
| Has the family been away for the day out to somewhere different **in the last 6 months** (town/into town/ to the seaside/day trip)? | ☐ |
| Has your child had a friend to visit **in the last 6 months**? | ☐ |
| Has your child been to visit relatives or friends as a treat for her/him **in the last 6 months**? | ☐ |

**Are there any other things you have done as a family/with your child in the last:**

**Week**

_____

_____

_____

**Month**

_____

_____

_____

**Last 6 months**

_____

_____

_____

_____

_____

_____

40

# **Family Activity**

## SCALE FOR CHILDREN AGED 7 TO 12

Could you let me know the sort of things you do as a family, or with your child/children both regularly and in the last year. Some examples of the kind of activities you may have done are listed below.

If you have done any of these activities **within the time-scale written in bold**, please tick in the box provided.

You may also like to mention other activities you have done in the space provided at the bottom of the page.

| | Activity if YES, please tick |
|---|:---:|
| Had a friend of your child to visit – **in the last month**? | ☐ |
| Had a birthday celebration (i.e. party/cake)? | ☐ |
| Been to the cinema/museum/zoo/panto/local event – **in the last 3 months**? | ☐ |
| Been swimming/skating/other (participant) sport – **in the last 3 months**? | ☐ |
| Been away on holiday with the family/to the seaside – **in the past year**? | ☐ |
| Been to the park/for a picnic/local farm – **in the last 3 months**? | ☐ |
| Has – or had – any pets **in the past year**? | ☐ |
| Attended any special classes/clubs i.e. football, dance – **in the last 3 months**? | ☐ |
| Been to stay with relatives or friends (without parents) – **in the last year**? | ☐ |
| Visited own friends (i.e. for a meal/for the day) – **in the last 3 months** | |
| Belongs to a children's library? | ☐ |

**Are there any other things you have done as a family/with your child in the last:**

**Week**

**Month**

**Last 6 months**

# GUIDANCE ON USING FAMILY ACTIVITY SCALES

## Background

1. The study of parenting styles has explored several different dimensions, including warmth/coldness and authoritarian/permissive approaches. Related dimensions are control and child-centredness.

2. Newson and Newson (1968) in their study of families in the general population, found that mothers felt strongly about their child's compliance because having children who behave well, and do not 'show them up' in public was important for their self esteem. At the same time, many mothers also recognised that they needed to concede some autonomy to their children.

3. Referring to 'child-centredness' Newson & Newson (1976) said:
   *'The keynote to this is the parents' recognition of the child's status as an individual with rights and feelings that are worthy of respect'.*
   One example cited by the Newsons was the extent to which mothers were prepared to accept their 4-year-old's claim that they were busy.

4. The concept of child-centredness underlies many schemes for observing parent-child interaction, and there is evidence that it is an important determinant of good child development.

5. What people do together and how they conduct joint activity is an important indicator of the quality of their relationship.

## The Scale

6. The Family Activity Scale is derived from a Child-Centredness Scale devised by Marjorie Smith (1985).

7. Child-centredness is seen to be reflected in appropriate opportunities for the child to be involved in autonomous activities of their own choice, or family activities that the parents judge to be potentially enjoyable or fulfilling for the child.

8. There are two versions – one for children aged 2–6, and one for children aged 7–12.

9. The scale aims to identify the extent of joint, child-centred family activity and independent/autonomous child activity, such as pursuit of hobbies and relationships outside the home, and selfcare.

10. The activities in the scale are intended to be relatively independent of family income.

11. It is not expected that families will provide all the activities or opportunities. To some extent this will depend on the characteristics of the child and the context of the family.

12. There are circumstances, for example low income families living in isolated rural areas and those with a disabled child, where access to some of the activities is not possible without additional support.

13. The scale is not intended to judge parents in a critical way, but provide an opportunity to encourage relevant activity, and assess the need for support to enable it to take place.

## Use

14. The scale has been used successfully with children as well as caregivers.

15. In piloting it was reportedly 'extremely useful' in initial assessment.

16. Used with both parents separately it highlighted differences in parent perceptions.

17. Used both with caregivers alone and with the children it helped with work on family relationships.

18. On one occasion the children's enthusiastic account of joint family activity gave weight to the view that there had been considerable improvements in the function of the family concerned.

19. When children took part it helped them to feel included, and was thought to have been confidence-building.

20. Specific items were useful as a focus for work to extend joint family activity. Where there is a lack of resource available to the family or a disabled child relevant support can be discussed, and if appropriate, provided.

## Administration

21. It is as always important to introduce the scale in a fashion that is appropriate to the family in question. With families that are new to the worker, the need to understand the family can be put forward. For those that are well known there is the need to get a fuller picture of how the family is at the present time – the questionnaire can be a way to broaden the focus of discussion. Where there a disabled child there is a need to understand

how this restricts family activity, and whether there are ways to ensure that the needs of all family members are met.

22. The scale will usually be used with main caregivers, but, as indicated, it can be used with parent(s) and children together.

23. The scale takes about 10 minutes to complete if used with a single adult, but discussion or any relevant work that develops will naturally take longer.

## Scoring

24. Each item is scored 1 if it has occurred, or 0 if it did not, and the item scores are summed to give a total score from 0–11 for the list of specific activities, and 0–3 for the items at the bottom of the scale, which allow for activities that have not been specified.

25. To be scored the interviewer must satisfy themselves that the motivation for the action was from the parents and that it was for the child(ren)'s enjoyment or stimulation. For example, staying with the grandmother as a treat during the holidays would count, but staying with a relative because the parents were going on holiday would not. Family pets only count if the child has a special responsibility for looking after them, otherwise only pets 'belonging to the child count'.

26. There is not cut-off score. The questionnaire is scored on a continuum: the higher the score, the more child-centred are the family activities.

27. Formal scoring – adding up the number of activities that have occurred in the specified time periods – can give a general indication of family child-centredness, but parental attitude to the various possibilities on the list, and their motivation to provide suitable opportunities, will contribute to the overall assessment.

28. In evaluating the meaning of the scoring and family circumstances, the development of the child and presence/absence of disability will all need to be considered.

## Reference

Smith M (1985) *The Effects of Low Levels of Lead on Urban Children: The relevance of social factors*. Ph.D. Psychology, University of London.

# Alcohol
# Use
## QUESTIONNAIRE

# Alcohol Use – QUESTIONNAIRE

Please circle the answer most relevant to you

1. **How often do you have a drink containing alcohol?**

   NEVER    MONTHLY OR    TWO TO FOUR    TWO OR THREE    FOUR OR MORE
            LESS          TIMES A MONTH   TIMES A WEEK    TIMES A WEEK

2. **How many drinks containing alcohol do you have on a typical day when you are drinking?**

   1 or 2    3 or 4    5 or 6    7 to 9    10 or more

3. **How often during the past year have you found that you were not able to stop drinking once you had started?**

   NEVER    LESS THAN    MONTHLY    WEEKLY    DAILY, OR
            MONTHLY                           ALMOST DAILY

4. **How often during the past year have you failed to do what was normally expected of you because of drinking?**

   NEVER    LESS THAN    MONTHLY    WEEKLY    DAILY, OR
            MONTHLY                           ALMOST DAILY

5. **Has a relative or friend, doctor or other health worker been concerned about your drinking or suggested you cut down?**

   NO    YES,            YES
         BUT NOT IN THE  DURING THE
         PAST YEAR       PAST YEAR

# ALCOHOL USE QUESTIONNAIRE

## Background

1. Alcohol misuse is estimated to be present in about 6% of primary carers, ranking it third in frequency behind major depression and generalised anxiety. Higher rates are found in certain localities, particularly amongst parents known to Social Services Departments.

2. Drinking alcohol affects different individuals in different ways. For example, some people may be relatively unaffected by the same amount of alcohol that incapacitates others.

3. The primary concern therefore is not the amount of alcohol consumed but how it impacts on the individual, and more particularly on their role as a parent.

4. Drinking alcohol can affect a carer's behaviour towards their partner or children, even if their alcohol consumption is within the Department of Health's guidelines for safe drinking. This may be particularly true if the parent has a vulnerable personality.

5. Drinking alcohol may contribute to incidents where there is loss of temper or parental rows. Deep sleep due to alcohol may reduce the parents' awareness of distress in young children at night.

6. Children of parents who misuse alcohol are more likely to have: developmental delays, social problems, emotional detachment, and delinquency.

7. Research has found that individuals who misuse alcohol are more likely to have a parent or relative who misused alcohol.

8. Children of alcoholics are reported to abuse alcohol or drugs more than children who have grown up with non-alcoholics, and are 2–4 times more likely to have a psychiatric disorder.

## The Questionnaire

9. This questionnaire has been found to be effective in detecting adults with alcohol disorders and those with hazardous drinking.

10. The questionnaire is designed to be self administered. Research has found that adults may be more honest in completing this type of questionnaire than in a face-to-face interview.

11. The questionnaire can be scored (see overleaf), but **should be viewed primarily as a tool** to help to raise the subject of alcohol, and to provide the opportunity to address any issues that may arise, particularly in the responses to questions 3, 4 and 5.

12. The questionnaire covers:
    – Frequency of alcohol consumption (question 1)
    – Number of drinks consumed in a typical day (question 2)
    – Ability to control drinking (question 3)
    – Failure to carry out expected tasks as consequence of the effects of alcohol (question 4)
    – Whether others are concerned about the individuals drinking (question 5)

## Use

13. The questionnaire can be useful to provide a baseline, either at initial or core assessment or during ongoing work.

14. The questionnaire can help to detect drinking issues in circumstances where alcohol problems are not suspected. Drinking habits are often hidden, even from other family members.

15. It is important that the questionnaire is used as a basis for discussion of drinking patterns. For example, it may be useful to explore with carers how they manage their children when they are drinking. If they go the pub – what happens to the children?

16. Where the worker is uncertain how to interpret the response to the questionnaire they should consult a professional who is experienced in this field.

## Administration

17. The introduction of the questionnaire will have to be carefully planned, particularly with carers from communities where the use of alcohol is frowned upon. One approach is to explain that it is important to understand families' approach to drinking alcohol, and that asking parents to fill out a questionnaire can be a useful starting point for discussion. It can be emphasised that the worker is not for or against drinking, but from the children's point of view it is helpful to know what part it plays in day to day family life.

18. Although designed to be self-administered, the questionnaire can also be used as a series of initial probes for use by the worker.

## Scoring

**Question 1**: Never = **0**,  Monthly or less =**1**,  Two to four times a month = **2**,
Two or three times a week = **3**,  Four or more times a week = **4**

**Question 2**: 1 or 2 = **0**,  3 or 4 = **1**,  5 or 6 = **2**,  7 to 9 = **3**,  10 or more = **4**

**Question 3**: Never = **0**,  Less than monthly = **1**,  Monthly = **2**,  Weekly = **3**,
Daily or almost daily = **4**.

**Question 4**: Never = **0**,  Less than monthly = **1**,  Monthly = **2**,  Weekly = **3**,
Daily or almost daily = **4**.

**Question 5**: No = **0**, Yes, but not in the past year = **2**, Yes during the past year = **4**.

## Interpretation of Scoring

1. A score of 5 or more indicates that there may be an alcohol problem, and that there should be fuller evaluation. It needs to be remembered that although people may be more honest filling in a questionnaire than face to face, they are still likely to underestimate consumption and effects.

2. If questions 3, 4 or 5 are checked as other than *No* or *Never* there is likely to be concern that the pattern of drinking may be having an impact on the children.

3. Interpretation may be helped by looking at the Department of Health guidelines.

   **The Department of Health guidelines for safe drinking state that:**

   **For men**, drinking between 3 and 4 units a day or less indicates no significant risk to health (1 unit = approximately ½ a pint of beer, 1 measure of spirit, or 1 glass of wine). Regularly drinking 4 our more units of alcohol a day indicates an increased risk to health.

   **For women**, drinking between 2 and 3 units a day or less, indicates no significant risk to health. Regularly drinking over 3 units a day signifies an increased risk to health.

## Reference:

Piccinelli M, Tessari E, Bortolomasi M, Piasere O, Semenzin M, Garzotto N & Tansella M (1997) Efficacy of the alcohol use disorders identification test as a screening tool for hazardous alcohol intake and related disorders in primary care: A validity study. *British Medical Journal*. **514**: 420–424.

# References

Birleson P (1980) The validity of depressive disorder in childhood and the development of a self-rating scale: A research report. *Journal of Child Psychology & Psychiatry.* **22**: 73–88.

Brugha T, Bebington P, Tennant C and Hurry J (1985) The list of threatening experiences: A subset of 12 life event categories with considerable long-term contextual threat. *Psychological Medicine.* **15**: 189–194.

Crnic K A & Greenberg M T (1990) Minor parenting stresses with young children. *Child Development.* **61**: 1628–1637.

Crnic K A & Booth C L (1991) Mothers' and fathers' perceptions of daily hassles of parenting across early childhood. *Journal of Marriage and the Family.* **53**: 1043–1050.

Davie C E, Hutt S J, Vincent E and Mason M (1984) *The young child at home.* NFER-Nelson, Windsor.

Department of Health, Department for Education and Employment, Home Office (2000) *The Framework for the Assessment of Children in Need and their Families.* The Stationery Office, London.

Goodman R (1997) The Strengths and Difficulties Questionnaire: A Research Note. *Journal of Child Psychology and Psychiatry.* **38**: 581–586.

Goodman R, Meltzer H and Bailey V (1998) The strengths and difficulties questionnaire: A pilot study on the validity of the self-report version. *European Child and Adolescent Psychiatry.* **7**: 125–130.

Piccinelli M, Tessari E, Bortolomasi M, Piasere O, Semenzin M, Garzotto N and Tansella M (1997) Efficacy of the alcohol use disorders identification test as a screening tool for hazardous alcohol intake and related disorders in primary care: A validity study. *BritishMedical Journal.* **514**: 420–424.

Smith M A (1985) *The Effects of Low Levels of Lead on Urban Children: The relevance of social factors.* Ph.D. Psychology, University of London.

Snaith R P, Constantopoulos A A, Jardine M Y and McGuffin P (1978) A clinical scale for the self-assessment of irritability. *British Journal of Psychiatry.* **132**: 164–171.

# Acknowledgements

The Department of Health is grateful to the professionals whose names are listed in the references for their permission to use their respective questionnaires and scales in this pack, and for agreeing to some amendments which enabled the instruments to be customised.

We acknowledge with thanks the social services staff who managed and participated in this study, and advised us on how best to present and use the materials. In particular, we thank the children and families whose feedback was invaluable in refining the scales and questionnaires and suggesting how they might be best used. We are grateful also to Steve Walker and Carol Wickes for their creative assistance with design and presentation.

### In the Chair of the Development Group

| | |
|---|---|
| Jenny Gray | Social Services Inspector, Department of Health |

### Consultants to the Project

| | |
|---|---|
| Dr Arnon Bentovim | Consultant, Child and Family Psychiatrist, The London Child and Family Consultation Service and Honorary Consultant, Institute of Child Health, Great Ormond Street Hospital. |
| Liza Bingley Miller | Social Work Consultant (from November 1998) |
| Professor Antony Cox | Emeritus Professor of Child and Adolescent Psychiatry, Guy's, King's College and St Thomas' Hospitals Medical School |
| Natalie Silverdale | Research Assistant, Lambeth Healthcare NHS Trust (until December 1998) |
| Dr Marjorie Smith | Deputy Director, The Thomas Coram Research Unit |

### Members of the Development Group

| | |
|---|---|
| Rohan Barnet | Essex Social Services Department (from July 1998) |
| Rita Crowne | Service Manager, Bournemouth Borough Council |
| Ann Goldsmith | Children's Assessment and Family Support County Manager, Essex Social Services Department (until July 1998) |
| John Griffen | Children with Disabilities Team, London Borough of Westminster |

| | |
|---|---|
| Ann Gross | Section Head – Child Protection, Department of Health (until September 1998) |
| Maurice Lindsay | Bath and North East Somerset Social Services Department |
| Steve Walker | Training and Development Manager, Kingston upon Thames Social Services Department |